VINTAGE CHARM
COLORING BOOK

HEATHER DAVULCU

DESIGN ORIGINALS
an Imprint of Fox Chapel Publishing
www.d-originals.com

It's Time to Start Coloring!

We're so glad you've picked up this coloring book, because we know you're going to find exactly what you're looking for here! Whether you're an experienced colorist or a beginner, whether you want to calm your mind or unleash your creativity, whether you just want to color or go crazy with crafting, this book has you covered, and here's why!

Need some advice? No problem! If you're a beginner, you'll learn everything you need to know to get started, from supplies to colorful inspiration. If you'd like a little help, we've provided guided coloring pages in the center of the book that start you off with a suggested color palette, finished example, and encouraging words. There's no need to feel intimidated!

Feeling creative? If you're looking for something new, check out our patterning and coloring techniques. Learn all about tangling and pumping up your pages with shading and blending. If you're feeling crafty, take a look at our ideas for craft projects incorporating colored pages.

Need to unwind? We get it! Every single page in this book was developed and hand-drawn by the author to give you the maximum benefits possible from coloring the images. By working with these designs, we know you are going to become relaxed, energized, and focused!

We know this book is going to give you exactly what you need: a little relaxation, some crafty ideas, and loads of coloring. What are you waiting for? It's time to get started!

MEET HEATHER

Heather Davulcu always planned on becoming an artist—from the time she was a little girl she just wanted to draw. She studied fashion and costume design at the University of Texas at Austin and worked in this field before starting a mural painting business. Heather's recent work focuses on illustration and licensing. Her latest collections are inspired by her background in fashion and costume.

Frame your designs for beautiful home accents.

ISBN 978-1-4972-0237-5

This edition created especially for Michaels Stores by New Design Originals, an imprint of Fox Chapel Publishing.

Fox Chapel focuses on providing real value to our customers through the printing and book production process. We strive to select quality paper that is also eco-friendly. This book is printed on archival-quality, acid-free paper that can be expected to last for at least 200 years. It meets the minimum requirements of the American National Standard for Information Sciences—Permanence of Paper for Printed Library Materials, ANSI/NISO Z39.48-1992. This book is printed on paper produced from trees harvested from well-managed forests where measures are taken to protect wildlife, plants, and water quality.

Fair trade principles should also be recognized when dealing with the creative and artistic community. We are pleased that our business practices and payments to authors meet the criteria to display **DO Magazine's Fair Trade Seal of Approval**. In order to earn the seal, all of the artwork must be original (not clip art or public domain material); the author must be paid on a royalty basis at fair trade rates (not piecemeal or via flat rates), meaning the author participates financially in the success of his or her titles; and the work of contributing artists must be acknowledged in print. DO Magazine: Color, Tangle, Craft, Doodle, www.domagazines.com.

© 2016 by Heather Davulcu/Artlicensing.com and New Design Originals Corporation, www.d-originals.com, an imprint of Fox Chapel Publishing, 800-457-9112, 1970 Broad Street, Petersburg, PA 17520.

Printed in the United States of America
First printing

Cover art colored by Helga Cuypers. Back cover art colored by Heather Davulcu.
Craft projects and guided pages colored by Razell Alcazar (p. 9 middle left, p. 71), Lisa Caryl (p. 2, p. 9 top right), Helga Cuypers (p. 77), Heather Davulcu (p. 3 coaster and bag, p. 5, p. 8, p. 9 top and bottom left, p. 65, p. 69), Heather Gibson (p. 9 bottom right, p. 67), Nadena Gibson (p. 3 journal), Annie Jump (p. 79), Lynette Parmenter (p. 73, p. 75).

The Benefits of Coloring

A quick Internet search on this topic will yield pages of articles with statistics and opinions from the scientific research and art therapy communities. If you want to learn all about the science behind the benefits of coloring, we recommend you check them out. In the meantime, here are some of our favorite reasons for picking up the colored pencils.

Coloring allows for personal and creative expression. When it comes to coloring and creativity, there is no right or wrong. It's all about expressing your creativity your way. There are no limits to what you can do and no judgment (you don't have to show your coloring to someone else if you don't want to). The creativity of coloring provides a break from daily routine and can even make us more creative in other areas of our lives, like at work.

Colored designs can be decoupaged onto countless surfaces to make unique home dec pieces, like these coasters.

Coloring allows us to unplug.
Coloring is totally screen free. It's just us, our supplies, and our creativity. Unplugging every once in a while is a great way to relax, focus, and recharge, so unplugging by coloring is doubly effective!

Coloring reduces stress and anxiety. Why? It's easy and therefore stress free. Even better, research shows that coloring actually relaxes the fear center of the brain, reducing stress and anxiety in the present, and improving the way we respond to stressful situations in the future!

Coloring brings about a meditative state.
Coloring requires some focus, but not extreme concentration. By occupying part of the brain with the simple, repetitive act of coloring, the rest of the mind is free to let go and relax, switch off other thoughts, and focus on the present moment.

Coloring connects both sides of your brain.
Coloring requires the logical, analytical side of your brain when choosing where colors go and filling in spaces in a design. It requires the imaginative side of your brain when selecting a color palette and making creative choices about patterning, shading, and blending. Doing these things together strengthens the connection between your right brain and left brain and also exercises your fine motor skills and vision.

Use your finished pieces to add a personal touch to cards, journals, and scrapbooks.

Transfer your colored designs onto fabric for custom bags, shirts, and more!

Coloring Supplies

As adult coloring grows in popularity, so has the variety of coloring supplies available. So, how do you choose? For coloring (and art in general), experimentation is the name of the game. What works well and feels comfortable for someone else might not work for you. When starting out, try a little bit of everything to get a feel for what you like and refine your choices from there. And remember, coloring is supposed to be fun and stress free. Don't get hung up on using the "right" marker. If you want some guidance, here are some things to consider when choosing coloring supplies.

Markers

If you like bright, saturated colors and quick results, you'll probably be drawn to markers. Markers yield vibrant colors and can cover a lot of ground quickly. For coloring, tip shape is an important consideration. Lots of adult coloring pages are intricate and have many small spaces. You want markers with points that will allow you to get into those tiny areas with precision. Markers with brush tips are very versatile, allowing you to color large spaces quickly while still being able to fill in small spaces. Even better, some markers are dual ended, with a brush tip at one end and a fine point at the other. Markers with bullet or chisel tips will make precision work tricky, but you can pair them with fine-tip pens in the same color—use the markers for large areas and the corresponding pens for detail work.

When it comes to markers, you will hear a lot of talk about alcohol- vs. water-based options. This refers to the contents of the marker—dye mixed with water or dye mixed with alcohol. If you're just getting started, you might be drawn to the more budget-friendly, water-based markers. As you grow more serious about coloring, you might be drawn to alcohol-based markers, which are built to last, often refillable, and are less prone to streaking, but they also come with a high price tag.

One great thing about professional-grade markers is that they are usually available for purchase individually. To experiment, try purchasing an inexpensive set of brush markers and one or two professional water-based and alcohol-based options. See which ones you like working with the most.

Colored Pencils

If you love adding depth and dimension to a colored design with shading and blending, colored pencils are the perfect fit for you. While high-quality markers *can* be layered and blended, colored pencils were *made* for this.

When purchasing colored pencils, point strength is an important consideration. This refers to how hard or soft the pigment within the pencil is. If you want to do lots of layering and blending, you'll appreciate pencils with soft point strength. These will provide a creamy application and cover large areas easily, but they will not hold a sharp point for long, so you'll have to do a fair amount of sharpening for detail work. If you want pencils that will get into all of the tiny spaces on your coloring page, you'll like pencils with hard point strength. These will stay sharper longer, giving you the best precision, but they will be more difficult to blend.

As you grow more serious about coloring, you might be looking for ways to create unique effects. Watercolor pencils give your piece a painted watercolor look without the need for painting expertise. You apply color with the pencils and then add water to create the painted effect. If you just want to color, though, regular colored pencils are all you need.

Like markers, colored pencils come at a variety of price points. To experiment, try purchasing an inexpensive student-grade set along with a few individual options at a higher price point. Purchase a variety of point strengths—soft, medium, and hard—to determine your preference.

Pens

If you love adding special touches to your coloring, pens are for you. With their fine points, regular colored pens can be used to color tiny spaces that your markers cannot get into, while paint pens and gel pens can be used to add patterning and accents on top of a piece that's already been colored.

If you really enjoy patterning, try purchasing one or two felt-tip pens to add doodles and details to a coloring page. You can pattern a design before coloring, or add the patterning to open areas like the background after coloring.

For special effects and accents, gel pens and paint pens are the way to go. Because their ink is opaque, these pens can be used to accent areas on pieces already colored with markers or colored pencils. Beyond that, you can purchase gel pens and paint pens in endless varieties, including metallic, sparkle, and neon, even glow in the dark! If you're not sure about the power of pens, purchase a white gel pen or paint pen and try using it to add accents to a colored design. We're sure you'll be back at the craft store looking for more!

Coloring Techniques

There are so many cool things you can do with a coloring page besides coloring it. You can make the design your own by adding patterning and flourishes, or you can add depth and dimension through shading and blending. Here are some techniques to try.

Patterning

Patterning might sound intimidating, but a pattern is really just a combination of basic shapes (like circles, lines, and triangles) that is repeated. And we can all draw triangles and circles, right? So we can definitely draw patterns. Here are some simple patterns for you to try.

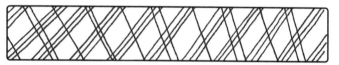

Lines. It doesn't get any easier! Draw them with even spacing, close together, far apart, or all three! Try drawing curved lines or lines that crisscross.

Checkerboard. Fill a space with a grid. Add something to alternating (or all) boxes in the grid—fill them in completely, add dots, add stripes, add hearts. Vary the spacing of the lines in your grid or try drawing it with wavy lines.

Circles. Draw them open or fill them in as dots. Make them all the same size or make some big and some small (like bubbles). Draw them in orderly rows or overlap them like ripples.

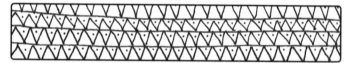

Triangles. Try adding triangles along a line on your coloring page. This is a really cool effect in and of itself, but you can take it further by adding dots or lines between the triangles or overlapping the triangles.

Need some help?

The Zentangle® method is a meditative drawing technique that uses simple, step-by-step patterns called tangles to produce unique art pieces. There are hundreds of tangles available online, a perfect resource for pattern ideas or step-by-step instructions. Try one of the tangles below on your next coloring page. To learn more about the Zentangle method, check out *Joy of Zentangle* or *Zentangle Basics, Expanded Workbook Edition* or connect with a Certified Zentangle Teacher (CZT) in your area (*www.zentangle.com*).

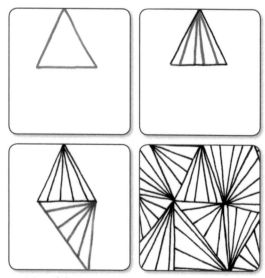

Munchin
An original Zentangle design

Flying Geese
Tangle by Suzanne McNeill, CZT

Shading and Blending

Shading and blending are wonderful ways to make a coloring page look more realistic, and they don't require a lot of expertise. Shading uses tints and shades of one color to add dimension. Blending uses multiple colors together to create cool gradations. Here are some simple ways to use shading and blending to make a design jump right off the page.

Go around the edges. Shading around the edge of a shape will add dimension. This can be done around a large shape, or around smaller areas within a shape. For example, you could shade around the entire flower (left) or just around the center circle (right).

Work from end to end. Try giving a shape dimension by working from a dark shade at one end to a light shade at the other end. The leaf at right is colored with three shades of green. To re-create this effect, select three shades of the same color: light, medium, and dark. Color the entire shape with the light color. Then, starting at one end, color two-thirds of the shape with the medium color. Then, starting at the same end, color one-third of the shape with the dark color. Go over the entire shape with the light color to help smooth the transitions between the shades.

Work from inside out or outside in. The same technique used to shade a shape from end to end can be used to shade a shape from the inside out (left) or the outside in (right).

Blend instead of shade. Blending follows the same steps as shading except it uses multiple colors instead of tints and shades of one color. For blending, you'll want a starting color, one or two transition colors, and a finishing color. For example, to blend from yellow to red, you'll want yellow (starting color), light orange (transition color), dark orange (transition color), and red (finishing color). Since you're working with four colors, mentally divide the shape you're working on into quarters. Color the entire shape yellow. Starting at one end, color three-quarters of the shape light orange. Starting at the same end, color half of the shape dark orange. Starting at the same end, color one-quarter of the shape red. Go over the entire shape with yellow to smooth over the transitions.

Gallery Wall

What better way to display your colored designs than by transforming them into a gallery wall feature! Here are some tips and tricks for creating a stunning gallery wall.

Map it out. How many frames do you want and in what size? Do you want an orderly grid pattern or a creative, eclectic layout? Will your frames be the same size, or will you enlarge or shrink some of your designs to fit frames of different sizes? Try out your design by cutting different frame sizes out of newspaper and hanging them on your wall to see if you like the look.

Pick your designs. Will you use only coloring pages or include some other pieces? What do you want to feature: your favorite designs, designs that are thematically similar, or designs with complementary color palettes?

Craft it up. If you're feeling extra crafty, try transferring one of your designs to wood or canvas. Experiment with color mats, or try cutting out small designs and attaching them to colorful paper for a pop of color in the background.

Pick your frames. Will all of your frames be exactly the same, or perhaps different styles but all in the same color? Maybe you want to mix and match black and white or choose bright, modern colors. Do you want frames with or without mats or a mix of both?

Hang it up. When all of your pieces are crafted and framed, it's time to hang them up using your chosen layout!

A Personal Touch

Coloring pages are a great way to add a personal touch to your home, your crafts, and even your gift giving. Check out the reverse side of each coloring page for a space designed for your creativity. Use it as a journaling page or a place to record notes about your coloring mediums and techniques. The page is made to be folded in three so you can mail your coloring page with a personal note if you're giving it as a gift.

Art washes away from the soul
the dust of everyday life.

—Pablo Picasso

Date   Name

Where you invest your love, you invest your life.

—Mumford & Sons, *Awake My Soul*

Date   Name

For there we loved, and where we love is home,
Home that our feet may leave, but not our hearts.

—Oliver Wendell Holmes, Sr., *Homesick in Heaven*

Date   Name

macaron pyramid

Everything in moderation, including moderation.

—Unknown

_____

_____

_____

_____

_____

_____

_____

_____

_____

_____

_____

_____

Date   Name

Our homes should inspire us to go
out into the world to do great things and then
welcome us back for refreshment.

—Unknown

Date

Name

You can never get a cup of tea large enough
or a book long enough to suit me.

—C. S. Lewis

_____
_____
_____
_____
_____
_____
_____
_____
_____
_____
_____

Date   Name

Never be afraid to sit awhile and think.

—Lorraine Hansberry

_____

_____

_____

_____

_____

_____

_____

_____

_____

_____

Date   Name

Fill your house with stacks of books,
in all the crannies and in all the nooks.

—Dr. Seuss

Date   Name

There is Nothing like staying at HOME for Real Comfort

love

-Jane Austen

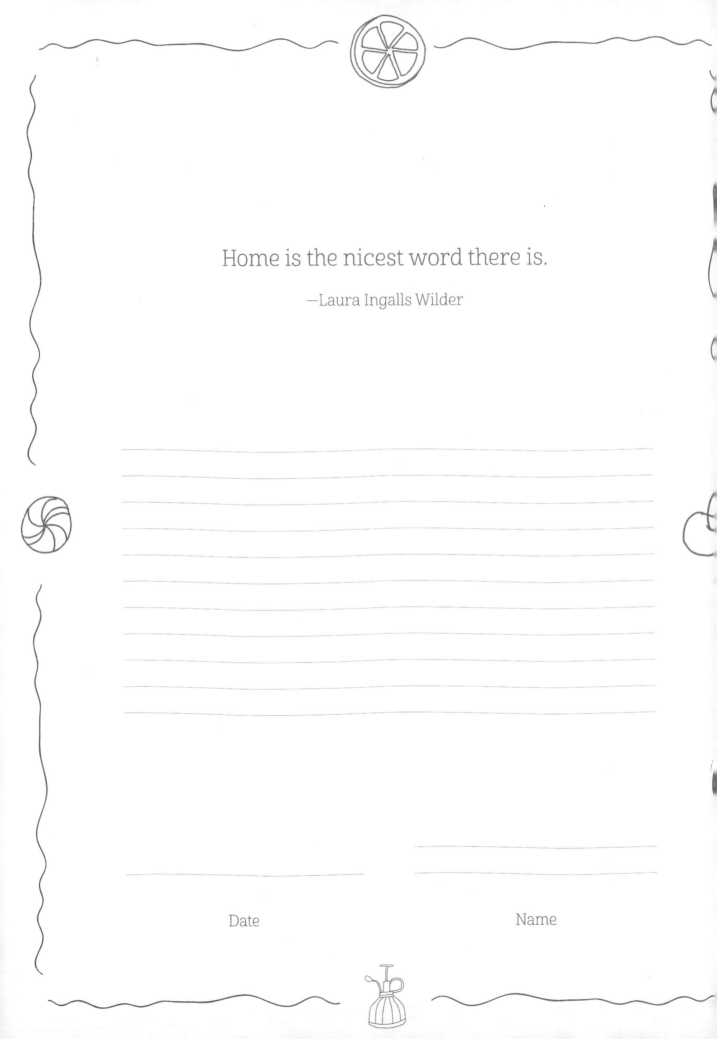

Home is the nicest word there is.

—Laura Ingalls Wilder

Date

Name

Nothing brings people together like good food.

—Unknown

_____

_____

_____

_____

_____

_____

_____

_____

_____

_____

_____

Date   Name

Plant smiles. Grow laughter. Harvest love.

—Unknown

_____

_____

_____

_____

_____

_____

_____

_____

_____

_____

Date   Name

HOME is where your Story BEGINS

SKETCH BOOK

Dreams and Plans

JOURNAL

FAVORITE POEMS

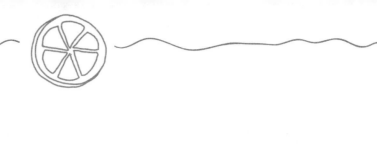

In every job that must be done,
there is an element of fun.

—"A Spoonful of Sugar," *Mary Poppins*

Date

Name

Less house. More home.

—Unknown

Everything is magical when you see
it with your heart.

—Unknown

Date   Name

Try lots of yellows, golds, and browns to make the pies in this image look like they're straight out of the oven. Introduce contrasting pops of color like purple and green.

The best things in life are sweet.

—Unknown

WELCOME

Sweet Home

mail

home

Try using a primary color scheme
with one or two additional accent colors.

Open different doors, you may find a you there that you never knew was yours. Anything can happen.

—"Anything Can Happen," *Mary Poppins*

gingersnaps

peanut butter

chocolate

Linzer

Black & white

jam

drops

Chip

biscotti

coconut

macaroons

pinwheel

Fortune

cookies

Meringue

whoopie pie

lace cookies

Macarons

Shortbread

almond

Florentines

snickerdoodle

cashew

Crescent

Madeleines

Take inspiration from the real world and color these treats to match your favorite baked goodies.

Celebrate we will, because life is short
but sweet, for certain.

—Dave Matthews Band, *Two Step*

Try pairing light or bright colors with deep,
rich hues for contrast and shading.

Every day is for flowers.

—Unknown

Analogous colors like blue, purple, red, and pink will pair well together. Add accents in green and yellow for contrast.

Nothing says home like the smell of baking.

—Unknown

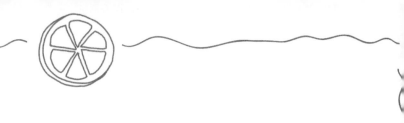

When life is sweet, say thank you, and celebrate.
And when life is bitter, say thank you, and grow.

—Shauna Niequist, *Bittersweet*

Date   Name

Home is not a place, but a feeling.

—Unknown

_____

_____

_____

_____

_____

_____

_____

_____

_____

_____

_____

_____

Date   Name

Something can be old, but it can be timeless.

—CeeLo Green

_____

_____

_____

_____

_____

_____

_____

_____

_____

_____

_____

_____

_____

Date   Name

Religieuses à la Framboise

Dacquoise

Paris-Brest

Mendiant

Galette

Tarte au Citron

Profiterole

Mille-Feuille

Clafoutis

Crème Brûlée

Canelés de Bordeaux

Mont Blanc

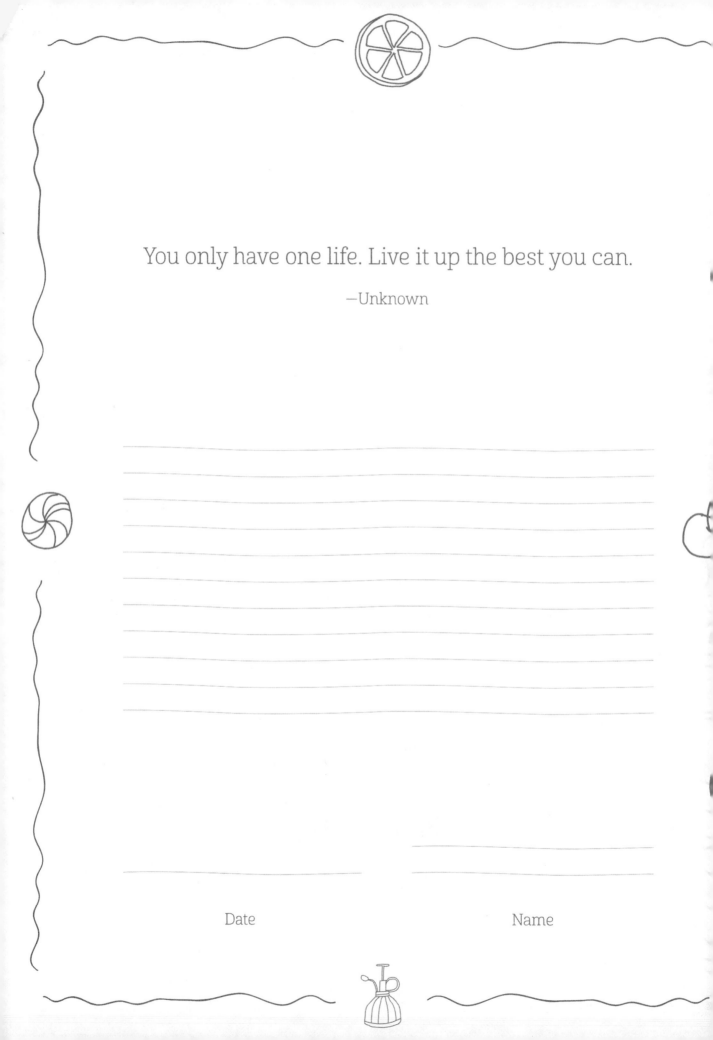

You only have one life. Live it up the best you can.

—Unknown

Date   Name

Together is a wonderful place to be.

—Unknown

Date   Name

Don't you know how sweet
and wonderful life can be?

—Marvin Gaye

Date   Name

Sewing is my SUPER POWER

Three grand essentials to happiness in this life are
something to do, something to love,
and something to hope for.

—Joseph Addison

Date   Name

Life is a great bundle of little things.

—Unknown

_____
_____
_____
_____
_____
_____
_____
_____
_____
_____

_____   _____

Date   Name

I am my own work of art.

—Madonna

Date   Name

The magic thing about home is that it feels good to leave, and it feels even better to come back.

—Wendy Wunder

Date   Name

All things great are wound up with all things little.

—Lucy Maud Montgomery

Date

Name

Simplicity is the keynote of all true elegance.

—Coco Chanel

_____

_____

_____

_____

_____

_____

_____

_____

_____

_____

_____

_____

_____   _____
Date   Name

Collect things you love, that are authentic to you,
and your house becomes your story.

—Unknown

Date   Name

Conchas

Cannoli

cinnamon Babka

Mochi

Pizzelles

Churros

Chinese Sugar Bun

Baklava

Kesari

Jalebi

Kolache

Mooncake

Hamantaschen

cream horn

Rice Pudding

Find something you're passionate about and keep
tremendously interested in it.

—Julia Child

Date   Name

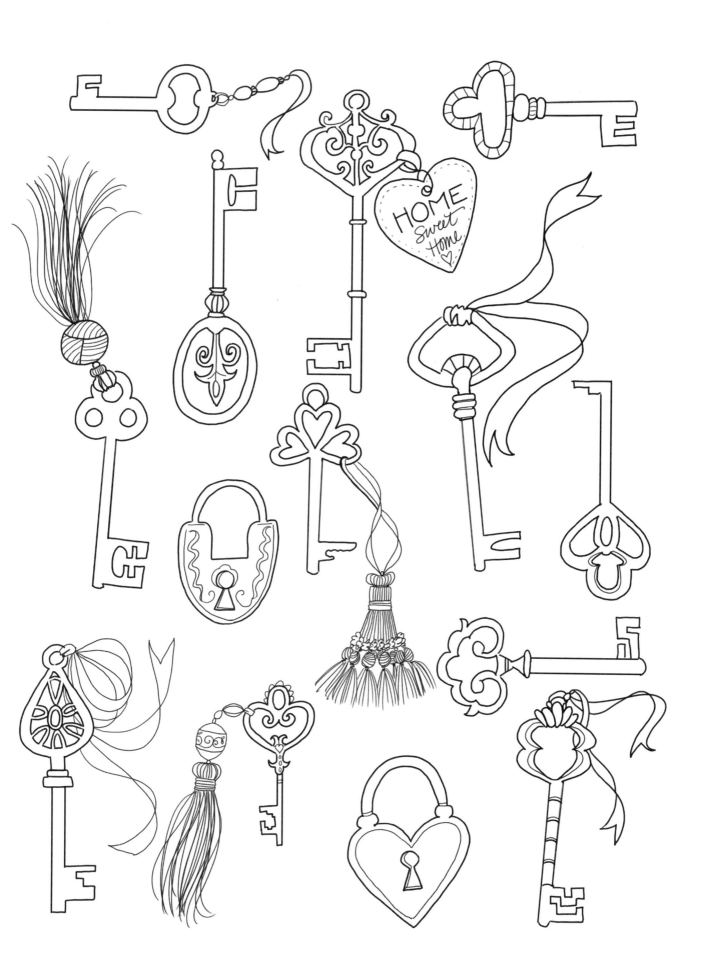

The best things in life are the people we love, the places we've been and the memories we've made along the way.

—Unknown

_____

_____

_____

_____

_____

_____

_____

_____

_____

_____

_____

Date   Name

Variety's the very spice of life,
That gives it all its flavor.

—William Cowper

Date   Name

Espresso

Italian

Butter cookies

pinoli

Sicilian

Almond cookies

Amaretti

Tiramisu

Rainbow layer cookies

Biscotti

cannoli

Laughter is brightest where food is best.

—Irish proverb

_____

_____

_____

_____

_____

_____

_____

_____

_____

_____

_____

_____

Date   Name

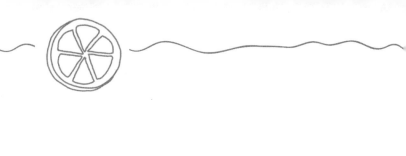

Clothes aren't going to change the world,
the women who wear them will.

—Anne Klein

Date   Name

Start the day with a smile
and end it with champagne.

—Unknown

Date   Name

Any time I get to go home is a joyous occasion.

—David Nail

_____

_____

_____

_____

_____

_____

_____

_____

_____

_____

_____

_____

_____

Date   Name